YOUR
SCOOBY-DOO
DETECTIVE BOOK
How to Be a Super Sleuth

by Randal Stevens

WORLDWIDE PUBLISHING

SCHOLASTIC INC.
New York   Toronto   London   Auckland   Sydney
Mexico City   New Delhi   Hong Kong

ISBN 0-439-14632-1

12 11 10 9 8 7 6 5 4 3   1 2 3 4 5 6/0

Printed in the U.S.A.
First Scholastic printing, January 2000

GROOVY!

JINKIES!

SCOOBY-DOOBY-DOO!

LIKE, WOW!

JEEPERS!

ARE YOU READY TO BE A SUPER SLEUTH?

Train your brain with the coolest doggy detective, Scooby-Doo, and the rest of the Mystery, Inc. gang. Test your talent for spotting clues. And put your decoding skills to the test.

Then fill in the casebook in the back of this book with your very own mysteries! Zoinks! Like, it's Scoob-tacular!

DETECTIVE NEEDED!

Can you solve these cases with the Mystery, Inc. gang? As you read the following three mysteries, make sure that you pay close attention! You never know where an important clue will come from.

THE CASE OF THE GHOST'S SLED

"Like, I don't know if we're going to make it," Shaggy said. The Mystery Machine was slowly creeping up a steep and winding road.

LIKE, IS THERE A CLUE ABOUT WHEN WE EAT, SCOOB?

"I took the van into the shop last weekend," Fred said. "I don't think there should be a problem."

"Wow, there is no one around way up here," Velma added.

"My uncle's friend Tony built his sled factory on top of the hill so no one would bother him," Daphne said.

I ROPE SO!

"Red racto-ry!?" Scooby-Doo barked.

"Like, wow, man. I only wish we had one right now," Shaggy added. "This would be a great ride down!"

"Maybe Tony will give you one of his famous A-One Sleds," Daphne said. "Those sleds are the fastest ones on the market."

"He is certainly far away from all other competitors," Fred said as he drove higher and higher up the mountain.

The gang saw the factory up ahead through the trees. It was a large building made of stone. A sign above the entrance read HANDMADE ITALIAN SLEDS.

"Do you think, like, he's got any food, Daph? I'm so hungry I could eat a whole pot of Italian pasta!" Shaggy said.

"Reah, reah! Rots of rasta!" Scooby-Doo added. His giant tongue licked his mouth in one swoop. "I rove rasta!"

4

"Here we are, gang," Fred said. Fred parked the Mystery Machine under a big oak tree. As soon as the van was parked, an older man rushed out of the factory's front door to greet them. He was clearly upset.

"Tony! What's wrong!" Daphne asked.

"Thank goodness you've arrived," panted Tony. "I've just had the strangest thing happen. My factory is haunted!"

"Like, as in haunted by a ghost?" Shaggy said.

"What happened?" asked Velma.

"Well, I was working on one of my special A-One Sleds when I heard strange noises coming from the storage room," said Tony. "I got up to look around outside, but I didn't find anything unusual. When I returned, there was a ghost running out the back door. The sled that I was working on was gone and so were my top-secret construction plans!"

"Jinkies!" Velma said.

"Like, who ever heard of a ghost wanting a

5

sleigh ride?" Shaggy asked.

"Or the plans to make a sled," Velma added.

"Well, gang, it looks like we have some work to do," Fred said.

Daphne held Tony's arm as the gang walked into the factory. "Tony, who else is working in the factory?" Daphne asked.

"Oh, business has been so slow this year. I'm down to just three employees," Tony said. "A young man named Carl carves the wood for the sleds. Patricia molds the metal blades. And Frank has been doing the painting." He sat down in his chair in the middle of the room. "I can't imagine that one of them would do this."

"They probably want to make a quick buck by selling your A-One Sled plans," Shaggy said.

Velma looked around the small workshop. "Do you make the sleds here by yourself?"

"Yes," Tony said. "My secret sled-making plans have built this company. I don't trust anyone else with them. That's why I keep them hidden in a secret spot underneath my oak desk."

Fred noticed a door with a sign that said TO FACTORY. "Do the workers need to walk through this door?" Fred asked.

"Yes, and it is quitting time," Tony said. "They should be coming through this door any second now."

The door opened and three people came through it. Each one petted Scooby-Doo on the head.

"What's going on?" asked Carl. He was a tall man with a small tool-box.

"We just have a few questions for the three of you," said Daphne.

7

"It seems that something very important was taken from Tony's office today."

Fred faced Carl. The young man had wood shavings on his clothes. "Do you know where Jack keeps the plans for his A-One Sleds?"

"I think that he keeps them in his office," Carl said.

"You must be Patricia," Velma said to the woman behind Carl. She had blond hair and a large yellow backpack on her shoulders.

"I don't know anything about any missing plans. And I'm late for an important meeting, so if you don't mind, I need to get going," Patricia said. "I'm barely strong enough to lift the sled blades, let alone that old oak desk, so there's no way I could be the thief."

Fred looked toward the third worker, Frank. Frank's gray hair fell in his eyes and he kept looking at the ground. "I take it you know nothing, either?" Fred asked.

"I'm awfully sorry that those plans are missing. But I was in the toolshed the whole day," Frank answered.

Scooby-Doo tilted his head and looked at the three suspects. Then he looked at Velma who had a smile on her face.

"It looks like we've caught our ghost sled thief," Velma said.

"Right-o!" Fred added.

SOLUTION TO THE CASE OF THE GHOST'S SLED

Did you guess? It was Patricia! My first clue was her large yellow backpack. It was big enough to hold a ghost costume. Then she gave us the second clue herself! She said that she couldn't lift the heavy oak desk. Jinkies! Only the thief would know where Tony's secret plans were hidden. Patricia did confess, and the sheriff came and took her away. "I would have made millions by selling those plans to the Great Sled Company!" she said as she got into the police car. "If it wasn't for those pesky kids and their meddling dog."

Another case solved!

THE CASE OF THE HAUNTED HOUSE

"Mrs. Johnson needs our help, gang," Fred said. He walked over to his friends at the back table of the Burger Palace. "I just got a call from her. She thinks that her house is haunted!"

Shaggy took a bite out of his giant sandwich as Scooby-Doo yelled. "Rikes! A rhost!"

"I thought that the Johnsons were moving to a new house," Daphne said.

"They are," Velma said. "But they need to sell their old house first."

The Johnsons were Velma's neighbors and friends

LOOK, GANG, WE'VE GOT ANOTHER MYSTERY TO SOLVE.

LIKE, I WAS AFRAID HE WOULD SAY THAT.

of the Mystery, Inc. gang. Everyone liked the Johnsons. Especially Scooby. The Johnsons kept a jar of Scooby Snacks in their kitchen for Scooby when he came to visit.

The gang drove over to the Johnsons' house right away. There were five people standing outside. Mr. Marmeld, the mayor, was talking to Mrs. Chasle, a neighbor from down the street with her son, Arthur. And Mr. Zotler, an architect, was talking to Mr. Johnson.

"I just don't understand this," Mrs. Chasle said as she waved her cane. "I have lived on this street for forty years and never once heard of a ghost!"

"Now, Mother," Arthur said. "Don't upset yourself." He wrapped his green scarf around his neck and blew on his hands to keep them warm.

"Arthur, maybe you shouldn't try to buy a house in this haunted neighborhood," Mrs. Chasle said.

"Yes," Mr. Marmeld sighed. "Who wants to live in a haunted neighborhood?"

"The house is not haunted," Mr. Zotler said. "I built this house."

Fred introduced everyone and then went inside the house to find Mrs. Johnson.

"Thanks so much for coming," said Mrs. Johnson when she opened the door. "You know, we love this house so much, but we need to sell it. Mr. Johnson got a new job in another city."

"Well, don't worry. We're going to have to stick around and figure out this mystery," said Fred.

13

"Ghosts just don't appear without a reason," Velma said.

Suddenly the lights went out.

"Ruh-roh!" groaned Scooby.

"Oh, no, not again!" Mrs. Johnson said. "I have to go check on the kids upstairs." Mrs. Johnson ran up the staircase and left the gang in the front hallway.

"Like, I'm getting nervous!" Shaggy said. "But I know what will calm us down, Scoob."

"Food!" they both said at the same time.

"All right, gang," Fred said. "Let's split up and see what we can find."

"Like, I don't want to find anything but a cheese pizza!" answered Shaggy.

"Well, then, why don't you and Scooby

come with me to check out the kitchen?" Velma suggested. "Fred and Daphne will look in the living room."

"Rokay!" Scooby-Doo agreed. They followed Velma toward the kitchen.

"Jinkies! A clue!" Velma said as she bent down to pick up a green wool mitten.

Scooby-Doo spotted another mitten in the corner by the stove. He trotted over to Velma and handed her the clue.

Shaggy, Scooby, and Velma carefully entered the very dark kitchen. They stumbled around the room, not realizing that they were not the only ones in the kitchen.

"GRRRRRR," roared a voice.

RELP!

"Ruh-roh!" Scooby barked.

As Scooby stuck out his paws, he found something that felt like a refrigerator door. Maybe he could hide in there. He grabbed the handle and flung the door open.

THUD!

Fred and Daphne rushed in and shined their flashlights on a crumpled mass behind the refrigerator door. The ghost had been knocked out by the refrigerator door!

"Well, Scoob, you've done it again," praised Shaggy.

"Just think, Scooby," added Daphne. "If you weren't hungry, we would never have captured this ghoulish creeper."

"I don't think we'll ever have to worry about Scooby not being hungry!" Velma said with a chuckle.

Who do you think was haunting the Johnsons' house?

SOLUTION
TO THE CASE OF THE
HAUNTED HOUSE

The Mystery, Inc. gang figured out another mystery. Did you? Outside the house, Arthur was blowing on his hands to keep warm. When Velma found the green mitten, she knew that Arthur had been inside the house. He was trying to scare the Johnson family out of their house so that he could buy it very cheaply. He wanted to move down the street from his mother. Mrs. Chasle didn't know about her son's plan and was very disappointed in him. Mr. Marmeld took Arthur down to city hall. Another ghostly mystery solved!

LOOK, ANOTHER CASE!

I BET WE CAN SOLVE IT!

THE CASE OF THE FAKE HELMET

"Oh, my aching stomach," Shaggy said.

"What's wrong, Shaggy?" Daphne said. "Are you okay?"

"No, not at all," moaned Shaggy. "Like, my stomach is in pain from all that hunger."

"All right, Shaggy," Fred said. "There's a pizza parlor up ahead. We'll pull over and grab a pie."

"Rizza rarlor? Scooby-Dooby-Doo!" sang Scooby.

Fred drove the Mystery Machine to Vito's Pizzeria. As everyone piled out of the van, Daphne noticed a huge group of people in the parking lot next to the pizza parlor.

"What do you think is

going on over there?" asked Daphne.

"Looks like a flea market," Fred said.

"A flea market! Like, Scoob, stay away from that place. I don't think you need any fleas," Shaggy said.

"Ruh-roh," Scooby barked and headed back to the van.

"A flea market is just an expression," Velma said. "It's a place where people can buy and sell antiques and collectibles."

"I love flea markets. Let's go check it out," Daphne said.

"Good idea, Daphne. I'll go order the pizza, and while they make it we can look around the flea market," said Fred. "Maybe we can find something groovy for the Mystery Machine."

Fred ran into the pizza parlor and the rest of the gang entered the flea market. At the first booth, two men were having a loud argument.

"I don't think this is real," the older man said.

"This helmet is the real thing," the man behind the booth said. "This was a helmet used in World War I."

He held up the helmet for the older man. Then the older man saw Daphne.

"Let's ask these nice girls," the older man said. "My name is Colonel Buck Roblee. I collect all sorts of things from old wars. This gentleman, Joe Shippley, wants me to buy this helmet."

"This is a genuine helmet from World War I," Joe said. He

handed the helmet over to Velma to have a closer look.

"I don't think that this is real," Colonel Roblee said.

"This is genuine!" answered Joe. "The helmet came from Germany during World War I."

"Hey, gang!" Fred said as he walked over.

"Hello there," Colonel Roblee said. "I've asked your friends to help me with a bit of a mystery."

"Well, we are good at solving mysteries," Fred said.

Scooby licked Fred's hand. "Right!" Scooby barked and wagged his tail.

"Well, then maybe you can solve the mystery of where this helmet is from," the colonel said.

"Look," Joe said. "Here on the inside of the helmet. It says right here!"

Velma read the engraving on the inside of the helmet. "*This helmet is for my brave captain. Signed, Otto von Bismarck, December 3, 1918.*"

"Scoob, if I had a helmet, I'd give it to you," said Shaggy.

"Ranks, Shaggy," Scooby said.

"I have a hunch that this helmet is a fake, " said Velma. "I think that we should call the authorities."

"I do, too," Fred added.

How did Velma know that the helmet was a fake?

SOLUTION TO THE CASE OF THE FAKE HELMET

Did you see the clue? Look closely at the writing in the helmet. Why would a German leader engrave his helmet in English? Clearly, Joe Shippley had engraved the piece himself and was trying to pass it off as real. Joe admitted that the helmet wasn't genuine. "If it wasn't for those meddling kids and their dog, I could have made a lot of money!" Joe said.

Another mystery solved, gang!

BLINDFOLD FUN

This is a fun game that will make you appreciate seeing a clue. There are other ways to find clues.... You can feel, hear, smell, and taste clues, too! A good detective uses all five senses when on a case.

HOW TO PLAY:

Ask a friend to play. Put a blindfold over your friend's eyes. Then lead your friend around a room. Give your friend different things to touch. See if your friend can guess what an object is by feeling it. Try bouncing a ball or playing a note on an instrument and see if your friend can tell you what is making that sound. Then

ZOINKS! ALL THE LIGHTS WENT OUT!

give your friend something to smell like a lemon or a piece of chocolate, and ask her or him to guess what it is.

Switch with your friend so that you are blindfolded. Have your friend give you different objects to touch, listen to, and smell!

Just make sure that you are careful and only go in areas that are safe and easy to navigate with a blindfolded friend.

LIKE, WOW! THIS IS A GREAT ACTIVITY!

FAR OUT!

JINKIES! DID YOU SEE THAT?

LIKE, HEY, WHERE DID EVERYBODY GO?

SPOTTING A CLUE

As a detective you must be aware of things around you. You never know where a clue will show up! Try this exercise to see how good your detective memory is.

Stand in the doorway of a room and look around at all the furniture and other items. Have a friend keep time and only look for one minute. When one minute is up, cover your eyes while your friend hides or moves an object in the room. Now can you tell what is different? You can take turns and even time each other to see who can spot the change the quickest!

MEMORY TRAY

I REMEMBER THIS GAME!

Go around your house and collect a lot of small objects such as paper clips, string, buttons, or whatever you can find. They must be small enough to fit in the palm of your hand. The more items you collect, the more fun this game will be.

After you have collected everything, put the items on a large serving tray or table. Then place a napkin or cover over the tray. Give each player a pencil and a piece of paper.

GROOVY, LET'S PLAY!

When everyone is ready, the cover of the tray is lifted. Each player then has thirty seconds to look at what is on the tray. When the time is up, the items are covered again, and everyone writes down as many items as he or she can remember. The person who listed the most items correctly is the winner.

27

I HAVE A HUNCH ABOUT THIS MYSTERY.

TWENTY QUESTIONS

A good detective asks lots of questions. It takes practice to ask the right kinds of questions that lead to clues. This is a really good exercise to help you be a better detective.

You can play this with just one friend or you can include as many friends as you like.

Start off by thinking of a famous person. Tell your friends the initials of the famous person you are thinking of. Each player then asks you a question to find out the

DID SOMEONE SAY LUNCH?

famous person you have chosen. The answer to the questions must be either yes or no. Your friends can ask you up to twenty questions to try and figure out the identity of your person.

Here are some examples:

Are you living?
Are you over one hundred years old?
Do you like Scooby Snacks?

Have fun, and try and solve the mystery in twenty questions!

SCOOBY DOOBY DOO

WORD FIND

In the jumble of letters, see if you can find the words below. The words are vertical, horizontal, diagonal, and even backward. Good luck!

Scooby, Ghoul, Haunted, Mystery, Shaggy, Fred, Velma, Daphne, Jinkies

```
P O V S U W Q Z S R I
G H O U L B N L C A H
B A K R E D E T O R J
C U D P T B F G O C I
X N S S R L R H B O N
O T M Y S T E R Y A K
W E K G F V D S I N I
K D P G S Z E Z I P E
P H Q A D Q Z L V N S
Z E N H P A D C M M Z
O R R S N A O B R A I
```

See page 36 for the answers.

SCRAMBLED CLUES

HEY, DID SOMEONE SAY SCRAMBLED EGGS?

A big part of detective work is trying to decode a clue. The letters in the following words are scrambled. See if you can unscramble them and find out the coded word.

HUGLSO

◯ _ _ _ _ _

RASCY

_ _ _ ◯ _

OSCBOY

_ _ _ ◯ _ _

HOTGSS

_ _ _ ◯ _ _

NIALVIL

◯ _ _ _ _ _ _

YSTMREY

_ _ _ _ _ _ ◯

◯ ◯ ◯ ◯ ◯ ◯ !

See page 36 for the answers.

31

PICTURE DETECTIVE

The following four groups of pictures appear to be exactly alike. However, while they all seem similar, one of the pictures is slightly different from the others. See if you can tell which picture is different!

1   2   3   4

1   2

*See page 36
for the
answers.*

3   4

FIND THE SCOOBY SNACKS

Ode to Scooby Snacks

Pizza and roast beef hit
the spot.
So can a turkey
sandwich and a full
spaghetti pot.
But of all the things
that go into my tummy
A box of Scooby
Snacks is by far the
most yummy.

OH, I LOVE
THIS PAGE!

Use your magnifying glass to find six Scooby Snacks () hidden in this room.

See page 36 for the answers.

ANSWERS TO PUZZLES

Answer to Word Find:
page 30

```
P O V S U W Q Z S S R I
G H O U L B N L C O A H
B A K R E D E T O A R J
C U D P T B F G O B C I
X N S S R L R H B O A N
O T M Y S T E R Y N A K
W E K G F V D S I N P I
K D P G S Z E Z I V N E
P H Q A D Q Z L V N S
Z E N H P A D C M M Z
O R R S N A O B R A I
```

Answer to Scrambled Clues:
page 31

HUGLSO	GHOULS
RASCY	SCARY
OSCBOY	SCOOBY
HOTGSS	GHOSTS
NIALVIL	VILLAIN
YSTMREY	MYSTERY

Secret Code: GROOVY!

Answer to Picture Detective:
pages 32 - 33

GHOSTS: 3
HAUNTED HOUSES: 2
WITCHES: 1
ZOMBIES: 3

Answer to Find the Scooby Snacks:
page 35

Start keeping your own case files! A true detective always writes down suspects and clues. Record your mysteries here. Now you're a real super sleuth just like Scooby-Dooby-Doo!

Mystery:

_____

_____

Date:

_____

Suspects:

_____

_____

_____

Clues:

_____

_____

_____

_____

_____

Mystery Solved:

_____

_____

_____

_____

Mystery:

_____

_____

Date:

_____

Suspects:

_____

_____

_____

Clues:

_____

_____

_____

_____

_____

_____

Mystery Solved:

_____

_____

_____

_____

Mystery:

_____

_____

Date:

_____

Suspects:

_____

_____

_____

Clues:

_____

_____

_____

_____

_____

Mystery Solved:

_____

_____

_____

_____

Mystery:

_____

_____

Date:

_____

Suspects:

_____

_____

_____

Clues:

_____

_____

_____

_____

_____

Mystery Solved:

_____

_____

_____

_____

Mystery:

_____

_____

Date:

_____

Suspects:

_____

_____

Clues:

_____

_____

_____

_____

_____

Mystery Solved:

_____

_____

_____

_____

Mystery:

_____
_____

Date:

_____

Suspects:

_____
_____
_____

Clues:

_____
_____
_____
_____
_____

Mystery Solved:

_____
_____
_____
_____

Mystery:

_____

_____

Date:

_____

Suspects:

_____

_____

_____

Clues:

_____

_____

_____

_____

_____

Mystery Solved:

_____

_____

_____

_____

Mystery:

_____

_____

Date:

_____

Suspects:

_____

_____

_____

Clues:

_____

_____

_____

_____

_____

_____

Mystery Solved:

_____

_____

_____

_____

Mystery:

_____

_____

Date:

_____

Suspects:

_____

_____

_____

Clues:

_____

_____

_____

_____

_____

Mystery Solved:

_____

_____

_____

_____